mac 2001

Cartoons from the *Daily Mail*

Stan McMurtry **mac**
Edited by Mark Bryant

To my unborn grandchild, whoever he or she may be

First published in Great Britain in 2001 by Robson Books,
10 Blenheim Court, Brewery Road, London N7 9NY

A member of the Chrysalis Group

British Library Cataloguing in Publication Data
A catalogue record for this title is available from the British Library.

ISBN 1 86105 489 0

Typeset by SX Composing DTP, Rayleigh, Essex
Printed by Bell & Bain Ltd., Galsgow

Tory leader William Hague's claims in *GQ* magazine that he drank 14 pints of beer a day as a teenager while working as a delivery man for a drinks company in South Yorkshire were treated with scepticism in some quarters.

'Oh, Norman. I'm so proud. I think our Kevin's going into politics.' *11 August 2000*

The Roslin Institute, Edinburgh – which had cloned Dolly the sheep – announced that it would halt a £12.5 million, six-year project into the use of pig organs for transplant into humans after new fears were raised concerning pig viruses crossing species.

'Typical of the NHS – an hour before Arthur's operation and they decide pig-organ transplants are too risky.' *15 August*

As A-level passes rose for the 18th consecutive year – leading to accusations of a 'dumbing down' of standards – it was reported that for the first time girls had achieved more top grades than boys.

'To save you wasting any more time working out if you've passed – that's the gas bill.' *18 August*

A 33-year-old butcher from a small Yorkshire village went on trial for attempting to blackmail his former wife out of her share of their divorce settlement by threatening to show her parents home videos of their 'swinger' lifestyle.

'Norman. It's the couple from two doors down and the man from Number 23 – are we interested in five-in-a-bed sex romps after *Emmerdale***?'** *28 August*

Shadow Health Secretary Dr Liam Fox demanded tougher tests for foreign doctors entering Britain and claimed that many of the country's 30,000 overseas doctors – a quarter of the NHS total – only had a rudimentary knowledge of English.

'Jings, mon. D'ye ken onny basic English? Ah telt ye, ah'm fair flummoxed wi wee pokey pains behind ma sporran and ma hairts jumpin' aboot like a biled haggis!' *29 August*

As police recruitment figures fell to the lowest levels for a decade, Home Secretary Jack Straw introduced a huge TV advertising campaign to attract staff. Meanwhile, three Bedfordshire officers claimed £100,000 each for work-related stress.

'Thanks for offering me the job, but I found this interview extremely stressful – where do I sue?' *31 August*

French fishing boats blockaded Calais and every major Channel ferry port in a dispute over the rising cost of fuel which turned the M20 into a giant lorry park and left thousands of British holidaymakers stranded on the Continent.

'Have you still got the suitcases, Enid? I think the blockade must be over.' *1 September*

After Mike Atherton scored a century at the Oval in the fifth and final test match of the series there was a strong feeling that England could finally beat the West Indies cricket team for the first time in 31 years.

'Doreen, the unbelievable is happening – I think England have a chance of winning the test match!' *4 September*

A professor of evolutionary biology at Sheffield University published research based on studies of hens and female guppy fish which seemed to imply that women are genetically programmed to be promiscuous.

'Listen to this load of old twaddle, Sharon. Scientists reckon that women are naturally promiscuous. How would they know that?' *5 September*

There were calls for the resignation of Dome supremo Lord Falconer after he asked for a further £47 million from the Millennium Commission to rescue the ailing attraction, which had already soaked up some £600 million of National Lottery cash.

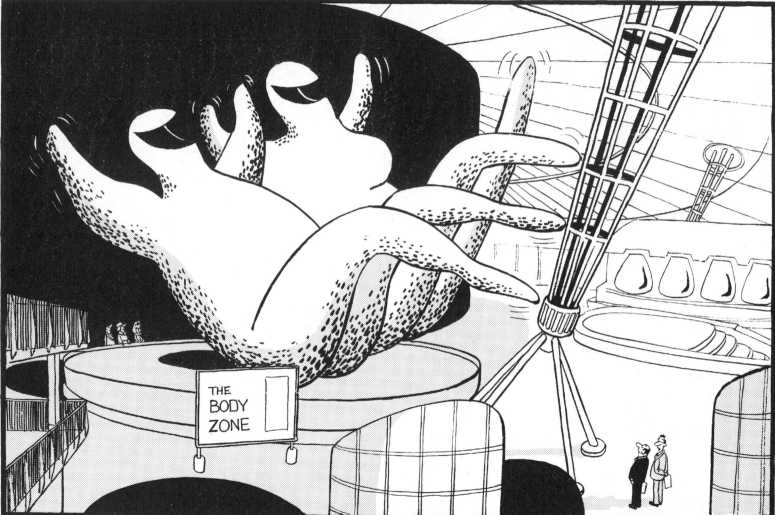

'They do that every time there's a fresh injection of cash.' *7 September*

'I'll spell it out for you just one more time, sunshine. Left at the lights, over the bridge, through the precinct and the garage is on your right. But you're wasting your time. They're out of petrol.' *12 September*

The fuel protests continued and with 90% of all garages closed, health and emergency services faced a crisis. Nonetheless polls indicated that most people supported the principle of cutting petrol costs.

'Rodney, darling. Don't smoke near the bath. I've filled it with four-star.' *14 September*

As the Government's problems deepened, the Minister for Science, Lord Sainsbury, reported that he had appointed a team of experts to examine the risk of Earth being hit by asteroids and to set up early warning systems like those in the USA and Japan.

'Look on the bright side, chaps. Things can't get any worse.' *19 September*

Following claims in Andrew Rawnsley's book, *Servants of the People*, that Chancellor Gordon Brown had lied about Formula 1 chief Bernie Ecclestone's £1 million gift to Labour Party funds in 1997, there were calls for his resignation.

'My advice is, stop telling porkies and don't go on TV for a while.' *21 September*

The seventh floor of MI6's new headquarters on the south bank of the Thames was rocked by explosions and windows were blown out in a suspected mortar attack by dissident Irish republican forces intent on derailing the peace process in Ulster.

'Listen, lad. If you're going to get along here, never ever slop tea into the saucer – and for heaven's sake smarten up a bit!'

22 September

British Airways suspended 11 short-haul pilots and three cabin crew after they were secretly filmed drinking 'to excess' only hours before flying, in a documentary made by Channel 4 TV's *Dispatches* programme.

'Heathrow? Left at the lights, over the bridge, then straight on – but before you go, sir, would you mind blowing into this?'

6 October

Shadow Home Secretary Ann Widdecombe's 'zero tolerance' policy on drugs – including mandatory £100 fines for possession of cannabis – lay in tatters when seven of her front-bench colleagues admitted that they had tried cannabis in their youth.

'All right, own up. Who slipped cannabis into Ann Widdecombe's coffee?' *10 October*

The Government granted £650,000 in additional funding after scientists at Nottingham University demonstrated a prototype pair of x-ray spectacles which could be used to detect underground water and gas piping and electricity cables.

'No wolf-whistles today – they seem preoccupied with work at last.' *13 October*

After lying unnoticed in the BBC's mail room for some days, a rare Second World War German 'Enigma' code machine stolen from Bletchley Park in Buckinghamshire was eventually discovered addressed to *Newsnight* presenter Jeremy Paxman.

'Sometimes it takes ages before Mr Paxman bothers to open his parcels.' *19 October*

Three years after the death of his wife Linda, former Beatle Sir Paul McCartney openly declared his love for charity organizer Heather Mills and kissed her in front of millions on the ITV programme *Stars and Their Lives*.

'Aw, isn't that nice. Paul McCartney declaring his love publicly. . .Doreen, darling, come and sit here.' *23 October*

In a study carried out on 63 heart-attack survivors at Southampton General Hospital researchers reported that a number of the patients had experienced sensations when technically dead, which seemed to support the theory of an afterlife for the soul.

'Ere, Norm! You had one of them near-death experiences once, didn't you?' *24 October*

Despite the fact that there were at least four reported sightings of a six-foot kangaroo at Beckenham Place Park Golf Course, near Lewisham, south-east London, no evidence of its existence could be found.

'I shouted "Fore" but it didn't hear me.' *26 October*

Following speed restrictions imposed nationwide after the Hatfield train crash, the rail network ground to a halt while lines were inspected for cracks. It was months before normal timetables were resumed.

'Oh, come on. You remember Daddy – he's been on a choo-choo.' *30 October*

As the rail delays dragged on and more fuel protests were threatened after the Government failed to reduce petrol prices, gale-force winds created havoc across the country and rivers burst their banks.

'Aren't you all glad you don't travel by car? I've heard there's going to be another fuel blockade soon.' *31 October*

The storms continued unabated, resulting in the worst flood chaos for 53 years. Meanwhile, the Royal Navy was forced to hire a German U-boat, S191, to patrol Plymouth Sound after its entire fleet of nuclear submarines was withdrawn for tests.

'*Ja, ja*. Ze milk from ze fridge downstairs, unt kettle unt ze telly. Vill zat be all?' *3 November*

As the floodwater rose in Britain, Republican Governor of Texas George W. Bush clung to a slender advantage over his Democrat rival Al Gore in a stormy contest for election as the next President of the USA.

'The weatherman says it's coming in from across the Atlantic.' *6 November*

The Queen Mother broke her collar-bone after a fall at her London Home, Clarence House.
Meanwhile, there was increased anxiety over whether Chancellor Gordon Brown's pre-Budget
Report would be able to head off another fuel-price protest.

'Really, mother. If you must panic buy, do get someone to help with the lifting.' *7 November*

In the event the Chancellor's Report gave some concessions to the fuel lobby but angered pensioners when he announced that the basic state pension would only rise by £5 a week (£8 for couples) next April. The floods continued.

'Hurry up, Arnold. A large bottle of cider and 12 packets of crisps. Let's party!'

9 November

A nationwide survey by the National Pest Technicians' Association revealed a huge increase in the number of brown rats in Britain and reported that a new breed of poison-resistant 'super rats' had begun to spread across the country.

'They don't worry me. Why do you think I've got a dog?' *10 November*

A 16-year-old girl from Cornwall who was too short to become an air hostess had both her legs broken and then stretched on a metal frame in order to increase her height.

'Promise not to laugh, Doreen, love. Silly Daddy's got it all wrong. You don't have to be eight foot to be an air hostess.'

14 November

The Queen reignited the row about the Royal Family and bloodsports when she was photographed wringing the neck of a pheasant injured during a shoot at Sandringham.

'Don't worry. You've got five seconds' start and if it's not a clean shot my wife wrings your neck.' *20 November*

Judith Keppel became the first contestant to win £1 million on the TV quiz show *Who Wants to Be a Millionaire*. A relation of Alice Keppel, mistress of Edward VII, she is also a cousin of Camilla Parker Bowles.

'. . .And on tonight's programme we have Charles from Gloucestershire, Elizabeth from Windsor, Philip from Greece, Anne from. . .' *21 November*

In the wake of research blaming deep-vein thrombosis and other ailments on cramped seating on aircraft, a House of Lords Select Committee report published new guidelines for the airline industry regarding the health of its passengers.

'Ease up on running on the spot, Betty. You're loosening the wing rivets.' *23 November*

There was a scandal when a Government report revealed that 100,000 people a year catch diseases in hospital and 5,000 die from these infections, which were blamed on dirty conditions and unhygienic practices by staff.

'Sorry I'm late. I've been visiting my husband in hospital.' *24 November*

Professional nursery staff were officially banned from telling off children in their care or using words such as 'naughty' and 'stupid' because of the alleged negative effect this has on them. Instead they were recommended to praise children's good behaviour.

'My troubles all started when I robbed a classmate, beat up the dinner lady and set fire to the nursery school. . .then a horrid, insensitive teacher called me naughty!' *5 December*

The recession-hit motor industry suffered another blow when Vauxhall closed down its main factory at Luton in Bedfordshire with a loss of 2,000 jobs. Meanwhile, there was renewed flooding in Kent, the Midlands and the West Country.

'Daddy, why don't people in this country buy cars any more?' *14 December*

Tory leader William Hague stirred up controversy when he attacked recent claims that the Metropolitan Police were guilty of 'institutionalized racism', adding that such allegations had destroyed police morale and triggered a law-and-order crisis.

'You're not obliged to say anything, sir. But should you utter, "I'm voting Tory" you can go home.' *15 December*

Home Office Minister Charles Clarke announced plans to crack down on speeding motorists, threatening to jail offenders who drove at more than 30mph above the speed limit.

'Yes, dear. I've got the turkey and the trimmings, but I was in a bit of a hurry when I drove away from the shop, and guess what?' *19 December*

'Aye, she's cold. But Morag's determined to get close enough to throw some confetti.' *22 December*

Prince Andrew spent a free holiday at an exclusive hotel in Phuket, Thailand, as the guest of sports equipment tycoon Johan Eliasch. As well as relaxing with topless beauties on the hotel's luxury catamaran he also played golf with his host.

'So anyway, at the next hole, there I was 300 yards from the pin in a gigantic bunker. I took out my three iron, then. . .'

5 January 2001

There were accusations of sleaze when it was discovered that some of the Government's recently ennobled peers – as well as the most favoured bidder for taking over the Dome – had made substantial donations to the Labour Party.

8 January

As Parliament debated the legislation on fox-hunting, Tony Blair decided to back down on his proposed 'marriage is best' policy after objections from divorced and gay Cabinet members.

'Honestly. Give them an inch and they'll take a mile.' *18 January*

In the event MPs elected by 387 to 174 votes to outlaw hunting with dogs in England and Wales.

'Isn't it wonderful? They voted to ban hunting with dogs.' *19 January*

Republican George 'Dubya' Bush succeeded Democrat Bill Clinton to become the 43rd President of the USA, the first time a son of a former President had taken office since John Quincy Adams did so in 1825.

'Here's your coffee, Dad. – Say, Dad, when do I get to sit behind the big desk?' *22 January*

A 56-year-old former teacher from Oxfordshire became Britain's oldest mother after receiving fertility treatment. She and her 55-year-old civil servant husband said they had felt lonely after their three grown-up children left home.

'Eggs. Let's have a dozen. *Click*. . .blue eyes. Blonde. . .*click*. . .buy, *click*. – Don't go nipping off to the pub, Harold. I'll need your contribution.' *23 January*

After Northern Ireland Secretary Peter Mandelson was forced to resign over the 'cash-for-passports' affair involving the billionaire Hinduja brothers, further evidence from the scandal began to cast doubt on the future of the Minister for Europe, Keith Vaz.

'Ah, Mr Vaz. The PM wants to know if the Hinduja brothers returned the little favours you did for them in any way. . .' *29 January*

A survey by the Mammal Society revealed that domestic cats were Britain's worst serial killers, destroying 275 million creatures a year including 55 million birds, as well as mice, frogs, bats, rabbits, squirrels and many endangered species.

'Perhaps if I made his catflap smaller he'd go back to just bringing in birds.' *2 February*

As it was reported that 75,000 asylum-seekers came to the UK last year, 24-year-old British yachtswoman Ellen MacArthur arrived in France in her £2 million yacht *Kingfisher* to become the youngest woman to sail single-handedly around the world.

'Get back! This isn't Britain!' *12 February*

Inspired by the film *Billy Elliot* – in which a working-class boy becomes a star ballet-dancer – Education Secretary David Blunkett pledged £35 million to fund after-school classes in dance, drama and music for deprived inner-city children.

'Aye. I'm bloody ashamed of him. He wants to be a miner.' *13 February*

On Valentine's Day the National Audit Office published figures which revealed for the first time that obesity in Britain had tripled in the last 20 years and that one in five of the nation's adult population was now overweight.

'I've waited by the phone since he vanished yesterday, mother. But still no message, no Valentine card, no flowers. . .'

15 February

As the Legacy property group withdrew its offer, Dome Minister Lord Falconer desperately sought new bidders to take over the ailing attraction, which continued to cost the British public £3.5 million a month in National Lottery money to maintain.

'I could tell the owner was desperate to get rid of it, so I made a silly offer.' *16 February*

After a significant rise in attacks on NATO planes patrolling the 'no-fly zones' in Iraq, US and British aircraft bombed Baghdad. Meanwhile, a book was published listing the 'accidental wit' of the US President, who had gained a reputation for malapropisms.

'There's some guy called Blair on the phone. Is he the one I'm bombing or do I have to be polite?' *19 February*

The Lord Chancellor, Lord Irvine, appeared to compromise his political neutrality as head of the judiciary when he invited barristers to a Labour Party fundraising dinner and suggested that £200 per head should be the mininum donation.

'Before I pass sentence, is there any advance on the measly donation you've promised to Labour Party funds? . . . £200. . .do I hear £400?' *20 February*

As the political parties geared up for the forthcoming General Election campaign, Tory leader William Hague pledged that he would reintroduce the Married Couples' Allowance scrapped by Labour in 2000 if his party was returned to power.

'Things are a bit tight, kids. So if the Tories get in I might marry whoever one of your fathers is.' *22 February*

Britain was quarantined by the international community and a worldwide ban was imposed on the export of British livestock and red meats following the confirmation of the first major outbreak of foot-and-mouth disease in the country for 20 years.

'Oh my God, Fred! You haven't been listening to *The Archers*?' *23 February*

As the number of foot-and-mouth cases escalated, sports events were suspended and footpaths were closed in farming areas. Meanwhile, the worst winter blizzards for a decade left motorists stranded and thousands without power.

'For heaven's sake, Harold, come back! We've been told not to go walking in the countryside.' *1 March*

With the deepening of the foot-and-mouth crisis, supermarkets and butchers began to run out of meat and there were fears of huge price increases as shops were forced to buy in stocks from overseas.

'Nut cutlets again! Surely there must be some meat in the house we can eat?' *2 March*

18-year-old Prince William went on a three-and-a-half-month tour of southern Africa during his 'gap year' between leaving Eton and starting his degree course at St Andrew's University in Scotland.

'Such a thoughtful boy. He couldn't bear to know we were short of meat.' *5 March*

In experiments conducted at the University of Arizona, a number of professional mediums achieved high success rates at discovering facts about dead relatives of volunteers. This was seen by some as being scientific evidence for their claims.

'Message coming through from someone called Ada. . . "Where the hell have you been. Arthur Swindley? Ten years dead and not a word from you. Typical! And have you painted that fence yet? No, You're always in the pub. . .and another thing. . ."' *6 March*

As the foot-and-mouth epidemic raged across Britain, American pop star Michael Jackson, on crutches and suffering from a broken foot, addressed 500 students at the Oxford Union.

'Relax, everybody. It wasn't foot and mouth. Apparently he always looks like that.' *8 March*

'Welcome to Hetherington Engineering, Mr Bodley. Now can we draw your attention to Clause 4 codenamed "Snip" in the contract you've just signed?' *9 March*

In an effort to prevent the spread of further contagion, Agriculture Minister Nick Brown announced that the Army might have to be called in to control the ever-worsening foot-and-mouth crisis.

'Marjorie. Some people are here about your sore foot.' *13 March*

As many livestock farmers faced ruin from the foot-and-mouth epidemic, Prince Charles personally pledged £500,000 from sales of his Duchy Original products and the Duke of Cornwall's Benevolent Fund to charities directly connected with farmers.

'Nice to see the royals are doing all they can for the farmers.' *16 March*

A knock-on effect of the foot-and-mouth crisis was the rapid decline in foreign tourists to Britain, with the industry losing an estimated £250 million a week as overseas visitors – especially high-spending Americans – boycotted the UK.

'Rare? We hadn't seen a tourist for so long, we had them stuffed.' *19 March*

Prime Minister Tony Blair announced that 2,000 extra GPs would be recruited into the NHS by 2004 and that there would be incentives of £5,000 for each surgery that cut waiting times and a further £5,000 for those which met agreed performance targets.

'All right, Mrs Frobisher. Get dressed again. Take two aspirin and I'll see you whenever I get back from Barbados.' *20 March*

A Home Office report advised parents to move computers out of their children's bedrooms and to monitor their Internet contacts as there was a danger that those who join e-mail groups and use 'chat-rooms' could be targeted by paedophiles.

'Katie, dear. Daddy says it's time to get thawed out for bed.' *22 March*

RoboDog, the world's most advanced robot pet, went on sale for the first time. Developed in Northamptonshire it could understand 60 different commands. Meanwhile, the aged Soviet *Mir* spacestation was finally decommissioned.

'See? You twiddle this little knob and it guides all that sophisticated gadgetry right to where we're standing.' *24 March*

In a desperate attempt to revive the tourist industry the Prime Minister appealed to the public to resume visits to rural areas, saying that the countryside was 'still open for business'. Nonetheless, foot-and-mouth precautions still continued in many parts.

29 March

Former high-street giant Marks & Spencer closed all its foreign branches and made more than 4,000 redundancies in a last-ditch effort to try and rescue its fortunes after disastrous losses.

'Sorry to do this while you're having such a hard time, but I'd like a refund on this dress.' *30 March*

In a *News of the World* 'sting' on April Fool's Day the Countess of Wessex made disparaging remarks about the Royal Family to a fake 'sheik', just before she and Prince Edward set off on a goodwill tour of the Gulf.

'Not foot, just mouth, Edward. Your mother rang to warn us your wife's got a chronic dose of mouth.' *2 April*

Home Secretary Jack Straw introduced emergency legislation to defer local council elections and the General Election until 7 June because of the foot-and-mouth crisis.

'Hello. . .Cooeee! I'm canvassing on behalf of. . .' *3 April*

A new Cold War loomed large after a Chinese fighter collided with a top-secret US spy plane and forced it to land on the Chinese island of Hainan. President Bush threatened tough measures if the plane and its 24 personnel were not returned.

'It's Plesident Bush. If you don't give his plane back he'll tell his dad and he bets his dad is bigger than your dad.' *5 April*

Prince Edward and Sophie – who had referred to the Queen as 'the old dear' – were summoned to Buckingham Palace after it was claimed that they were using tax-payer-funded state visits to drum up business for Edward's TV company, Ardent.

'Edward. Can you and Sophie pop round again? The old dear would like another word.' *6 April*

Former tennis superstar Boris Becker confessed on German TV that a brief drunken fling with a Russian model in a broom cupboard at a Japanese restaurant in Mayfair had led to a baby, the end of his marriage and a £2 million paternity settlement.

'I can't find my broom, Doris. But I think I just got Boris Becker's autograph.' *12 April*

In the run-up to Easter, it was revealed that some leading Conservatives were plotting to replace Tory Party leader William Hague with Shadow Chancellor Michael Portillo after the forthcoming General Election, irrespective of the result of the vote.

'You can come out now, Mr Hague. It's definitely only a chocolate Easter egg.' *17 April*

A leaked internal report by the Ministry of Agriculture revealed 'mismanagement and incompetence' by MAFF officials during the foot-and-mouth crisis. Meanwhile, Moroccan Abdelkader El Mouaziz won the 21st Flora London Marathon.

'**Problem solved, madam. If your husband was wearing blue shorts and was foaming at the mouth with blistered feet, MAFF had him put down about an hour ago.**' *23 April*

In the same week that the Attorney-General ordered Scotland Yard to investigate Saddam Hussein, the Government announced that teenagers on crime-ridden British estates would receive free CDs and trainers if they promised to stay out of trouble.

'Alternatively, Mr Hussein, sir. If you promise to give up your crimes against humanity, I have been authorized to offer you two new CDs and a nice pair of trainers.' *26 April*

The Government revealed plans for a Child's Trust Fund scheme in which children would be granted up to £500 each at birth, to be topped up by further sums at the ages of 5, 11 and 16 and available to be spent on 'worthwhile projects' at the age of 18.

'Congratulations, Mrs Macgregor. It's a boy. He's just popped out to the bank.' *27 April*

The Ministry of Defence was accused of wasting public resources when it was discovered that breast implants, sex-change treatment and liposuction were available to soldiers at the tax-payer's expense, despite cuts in manpower and equipment.

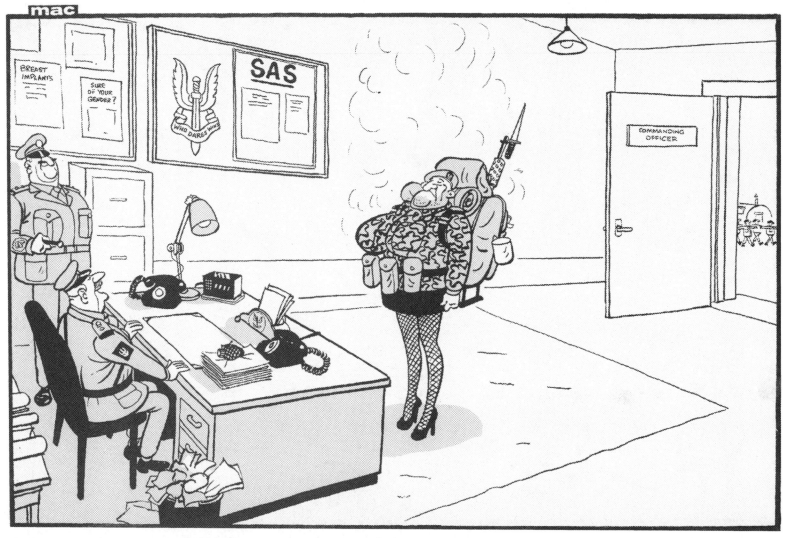

'To be honest, Perkins, we didn't think you were SAS material. But a 30-mile route march with full pack whilst performing a DIY liposuction and sex-change operation is quite impressive.' *30 April*

After last year's desecration of London by anti-capitalist and anarchist protesters, a huge police presence on May Day largely contained troublemakers but the Met's innovative tactics led to many compensation claims for infringement of civil liberties.

'Don't be too hard on the lad, dear. After all that planning for May Day, some horrid policemen infringed his civil liberties.'

3 May

Speculation that 71-year-old Great Train Robber Ronnie Biggs, who had suffered three strokes, would be allowed to return to the UK from Brazil after 35 years on compassionate grounds proved justified.

'I know it's hard after all this time, Lucan. But I may have to let you go.' *4 May*

In what was heralded as the biggest revolution in family planning since the Pill was launched in 1960, a US pharmaceutical company announced that it had developed a self-adhesive contraceptive patch which would be available from 2002.

'These patches really work – I'm getting a headache.' *10 May*

The Labour Party launched its manfesto, *Ambitions for Britain*, in which it pledged to smash the 'glass ceiling' that held the nation back and called for a 'marriage of economic prosperity and social justice' to allow the 'talents of everyone' to flourish.

'Wake up, Ron. That glass ceiling what's been stoppin' us fulfilling our potential has sprung a leak again.' *17 May*

Deputy Prime Minister John Prescott punched a countryside protester in the face and became involved in a brawl after he was hit by an egg on his way to address a meeting in Rhyl, North Wales.

mac

This cartoon was going to poke fun at John Prescott. But I want to keep my teeth – Mac. *18 May*

As the General Election campaign drew to a close the biggest fear of all parties was voter apathy.

'Drop!. . .Good boy. Next, Mrs Angela Payne of 4 Acacia Gardens. . .fetch!' *7 June*

In the event the election was won by a landslide victory to Labour. Gaining 413 seats in Parliament it was also the first time that the Labour Party had been elected for a consecutive full term. William Hague immediately resigned as Tory Party leader.

'Isn't it exciting? After all these weeks we're going to see Daddy again.' *8 June*

As the Duke of Edinburgh celebrated his 80th birthday at Windsor Castle, Buckingham Palace strenuously denied reports of alleged arguments between Prince Charles and his father.

'. . .74. . .75. . .76. . .easy, Charles. Not quite so high. . .77. . .78. . .79. . .' *11 June*

Following the resignation of William Hague, Shadow Chancellor Michael Portillo announced his candidacy in the Tory leadership race. A hot favourite, a feature on him in the *Daily Mail* was entitled 'Can He Bring the Tories Back from the Dead?'

' 'Scuse me, mister. Mum says if you can bring things back to life, would you have a go at our cat?' *14 June*

Other contenders who threw their hats into the ring for leadership of the Conservative Party included Shadow Defence Secretary Iain Duncan Smith, former Chancellor Kenneth Clarke, right-winger David Davis and Party Chairman Michael Ancram.

'Today you've got one Napoleon, a woman who thinks she's a sausage, a mad axeman and some poor souls who want to lead the Tory Party.' *18 June*

Using the latest technology, Professor John Burland, a British civil engineer from Imperial College, London, helped to stabilize the famous 14th-century Leaning Tower of Pisa in Italy, which had been close to collapse.

'You're right. It *is* Viagra.' *19 June*

It was revealed that, in order secure a legacy of £2 million from their aged mother, a 62-year-old Frenchwoman had given birth to a boy after receiving sperm from her brother, who had also simultaneously fathered a daughter using a paid surrogate.

' "Who's been sleeping in my bed?" said the surrogate daddy and uncle of the baby bear whose 62-year-old mummy had laid an egg given her by an American mummy bear so they could all have more porridge. . ." ' *22 June*

When asked by the Lottery Commission to explain why Lottery ticket sales had slumped, resulting in £5 billion less than predicted to spend on good causes, Camelot blamed 'Lottery fatigue', despite the introduction of new prizes and gimmicks.

'Hello, Camelot? Can your sales team think of another idea? We haven't sold a ticket all week.' *28 June*

In an attempt to combat the increased use of bad language in schools the Government introduced a controversial new scheme in which teachers were required to explain the meaning of swear words to children as young as 11.

'Please, Mummy. Don't let these old s*** eat all the f******* cake. I've just finished my b***** homework and I'm f****** famished.'

3 July

In preparation for his 'Picnic in the Park' open-air concert in London's Hyde Park, 25-stone Italian operatic tenor Luciano Pavarotti was hoisted on to the stage using a specially adapted hydraulic scissor-jack.

'I don't care what Pavarotti does in the park. This is wrecking our carpet!' *5 July*

There were fears of a 'designer baby' boom when it was announced that a technique pioneered in the USA which allowed parents to select the sex of their children, thereby avoiding genetically inherited defects, would soon be available in the UK.

'We could do with some fresh faces in the accounts department, Miss Winkworthy. Take this round to my house with some petty cash and ask my wife to order a boy, will you?' *6 July*

After an agonizing three days of delays, disruption and showers, British tennis No. 1 Tim Henman was finally beaten by Croatian Goran Ivanisevic in the semi-finals of Wimbledon. Ivanisevic went on to win the tournament.

'For heaven's sake. It was only a game of tennis!' *9 July*

There were calls to arm the police with water cannon after Britain's worst rioting for 16 years when 1,000 mostly Asian youths rampaged through Bradford after provocation by white racists.

'There are some men at the front door asking what you were doing last Saturday night.' *10 July*

Reports of a new technique to fertilize human eggs without using sperm, combined with news of a huge increase in the number of career women becoming single mothers by donor insemination, raised questions about the future role of fathers.

'I'm home, Daddy – guess what we did in biology today?' *13 July*

Michael Portillo's hopes in the Tory leadership contest nose-dived after he and his followers
were accused of disloyalty to William Hague during the General Election in a 'video diary'
shown on Channel 4 made by former Party spin-doctor Amanda Platell.

'**And now,** *Amanda Platell's Secret Video Diary, Part Two – Bathtime with Portillo. . .*' *16 July*

In the final poll of Conservative MPs for leader of the Tory Party, 61-year-old former Chancellor Ken Clarke had a clear lead over Iain Duncan Smith and Michael Portillo. Meanwhile, US President George Bush visited Tony Blair at Chequers.

'The Prime Minister's waiting for me at Number Ten? Then who the hell is this guy?' *19 July*

Novelist and former MP Jeffrey Archer received a four-year prison sentence for perjury and perverting the course of justice during his 1987 libel action against the *Daily Star*. At the original trial the judge described Lady Archer as 'fragrant'.

'We thought you'd like a cellmate – is he not fragrant?' *23 July*

After it was revealed that the UK has the longest waiting times for surgery in Europe, the European Court of Justice ruled that the British Government could not refuse to pay for Britons to be treated in other EU countries offering a quicker service.

'I'm sending him to Mongolia to have his hip replaced. How many stamps do I stick on?' *24 July*

There was a furious outcry and a record number of complaints to TV watchdog organizations when Channel 4 screened a spoof documentary about paedophilia in its *Brass Eye* series hosted and written by satirist Chris Morris.

'Some hilarious new material for the *Brass Eye* show has just arrived, sir.' *30 July*

In a pilot scheme to cut NHS waiting lists, West Sussex Health Authority linked up with a German medical group, GerMedic, to offer 50 British patients hip- and knee-replacement surgery at a hospital near Essen in Germany.

'Secretly I think Donald wishes he'd waited instead of having his hips done in Germany.' *31 July*

Scotland Yard announced that it would be issuing 'Taser' electronic stun guns to the police by Christmas. The US-made guns use laser-targeted darts to deliver a 50,000-volt shock capable of temporarily paralysing victims and have a range of 20 feet.

'Golly gosh, Sarge. You're pretty fast. Another split second and he would have fouled the pavement.' *2 August*

After the Home Office recommended that speed cameras should be painted orange the Chief Constable of Norfolk added on BBC Radio 4's *Today* programme that more warnings should be given about their location to encourage drivers to slow down.

'**You'd have thought painting them orange would've been enough.**' *3 August*

In a radical shake-up, Home Secretary David Blunkett announced that thousands of plainclothes police were to be sent back on to the beat to improve public confidence and that solo patrols would be introduced wherever possible to improve efficiency.

'City centre fairly busy, Sarge. Am watching juvenile male, slightly built Caucasian, tampering with vehicles and, 'ello, 'ello. . .just spotted dodgy-looking character trying to dispose of some hot goods.' *7 August*

As the film *Cats and Dogs* opened in Britain a paper was delivered to a meeting of the Animal Behaviour Society in the USA which claimed to show scientific evidence that dogs use at least four sound patterns – barks, growls, whines and. . . laughs.

'Poor soul. After the business folded and the house caught fire, his wife left him, then his cat died, his haemorrhoids erupted and he got run over by a bus.' *9 August*

Unable to reach hospital in time, a woman from Stockport, Lancashire, gave birth in a Kwik-Fit service centre, helped by the staff. Meanwhile, the NHS bought the famous London Heart Hospital, formerly privately owned, for £27 million.

'Don't worry, mate. She's in good hands. We've just been bought by the NHS.' *10 August*

Former Conservative minister Neil Hamilton, bankrupted by his lawsuit against Harrods boss Mohamed Al Fayed over the 'cash-for-questions' affair, hit the headlines again when he and his wife were accused of raping a 28-year-old mother.

'Good grief! Now what are the Hamiltons up to?' *14 August*

35-year-old Helena Bonham Carter, star of Tim Burton's remake of the 1968 film *Planet of the Apes* – in which she appeared in make-up as an ape – was one of the guests at the premiere of the film in London's Leicester Square.

'Before getting too involved, son. Are you absolutely sure she's Helena Bonham Carter?' *16 August*

The *Spectator*, quoting a 'well-informed Palace observer' claimed that the Queen had agreed to the marriage of Prince Charles and Camilla Parker Bowles after the Golden Jubilee celebrations next year, but added that she could not herself become queen.

'Hoskins. Retrieve one's hat from Mrs Parker Bowles and escort her from the premises, will you?' *17 August*

Princess Diana's former butler, Paul Burrell, appeared in court charged with stealing 414 personal items from her worth an estimated £6 million.

'My suspicions about Wilkinson deepen – he's just handed me a ransom note for the corgis.' *20 August*

French police reported that they had eventually captured 44 asylum-seekers who had managed to walk seven miles into the Channel Tunnel.

'Quickly, Mohammad. Quickly! Put another leaf on the line.' *3 September*

A book by Harriet Sergeant, *Welcome to the Asylum*, claimed that 400,000 illegal immigrants could be entering Britain each year but still Downing Street refused to police the Channel Tunnel, saying that it was the responsibility of the French.

'I thought if we let them slip in here too, Blair might start doing something about it.' *6 September*

Cardinal Cormac Murphy-O'Connor, head of the Roman Catholic Church in England and Wales, said that Christian belief in Britain had 'almost been vanquished' in favour of music, New Age movements, occult practices and green issues.

'Mrs Featherstone wants to know, if she sells her soul can she still do the flower-arranging on alternate Sundays?' *7 September*

Telecommunications equipment giant Marconi cut 2,000 jobs following bad management decisions and there was a public outcry when its chief executive received a £1 million pay-off plus £800,000 in additional benefits.

'Believe me, I know how you feel. I've been laid off too.' *10 September*

A scientific research study presented to the British Society of Gerontology suggested that regular sex 'eases tension and helps keep old age at bay'.

'Please, Doris. I know you're trying to help, but not now!' *11 September*

On 11 September the World Trade Center in New York and the Pentagon in Washington DC were attacked by passenger aircraft hijacked by terrorists. The main suspect for US Intelligence was Afghanistan-based Saudi dissident Osama Bin Laden.

13 September

As newspapers and TV in Iraq praised the terrorist attacks in the USA, saying that the Americans deserved them for 'crimes against humanity', US Intelligence opinion also began to suspect Saddam Hussein's involvement.

Sadman Insane *14 September*

The USA declared war on terrorism worldwide and launched Operation Noble Eagle to search out and destroy not only the perpetrators of the attacks on New York and Washington but all those who supported terrorists or gave them shelter.

The Ratcatcher   *17 September*

Scientists at the Karolinska Institute in Stockholm, Sweden, found that having sex makes men aged between 45 and 60 twice as likely to suffer heart attacks, and those who take little or no exercise are four times as likely to do so.

'Oooh, Arthur. You know how to please a girl – OK, now a treble somersault and I'm yours.' *18 September*

Following the terrorist attacks in the USA a general germ-warfare alert was put out by the World Health Organization. Meanwhile, new NHS star ratings were introduced to 'name and shame' Britain's worst hospitals, with the highest grade being three stars.

'You're the chief surgeon, Charlie. You tell him – we've been on germ-warfare alert for years.' *27 September*

Prince Edward came under fire again when members of his company, Ardent Productions, were found to have broken the general media agreement to respect Prince William's privacy when he began his studies at St Andrews University.

'Sophie, I've told you not to ring me when I'm working!' *28 September*

As the situation in Afghanistan became increasingly tense, ITV football commentator and father of three Ally McCoist made headline news when it was revealed that he had had affairs with actress Patsy Kensit and a 28-year-old air stewardess.

'Psst. Who exactly *is* Ally McCoist?' *2 October*

Following the disasters in the USA many airlines faced ruin as bookings fell off dramatically. British Airways announced more than 7,000 job cuts, Swissair grounded all its planes and many other companies were on the verge of collapse.

'You should pop down to Heathrow. They're almost giving them away.' *4 October*